Specific Skill Series

Locating the Answer

Richard A. Boning

Fifth Edition

SRA/McGraw-Hill
Columbus, Ohio

SRA/McGraw-Hill

A Division of The **McGraw·Hill** *Companies*

Send all inquiries to:
  SRA/McGraw-Hill
  8787 Orion Place
  Columbus, OH 43240-4027

ISBN 0-02-687952-2

10 11 IPC 05 04 03

To the Teacher

PURPOSE:

As its title indicates, LOCATING THE ANSWER develops pupils' skill in finding *where* sought-for information can be found within a passage. Pupils must carefully read and understand each question, grasp phrase and sentence units, and discriminate between pertinent and irrelevant ideas.

FOR WHOM:

The skill of LOCATING THE ANSWER is developed through a series of books spanning ten levels (Picture, Preparatory, A, B, C, D, E, F, G, H). The Picture Level is for pupils who have not acquired a basic sight vocabulary. The Preparatory Level is for pupils who have a basic sight vocabulary but are not yet ready for the first-grade-level book. Books A through H are appropriate for pupils who can read on levels one through eight, respectively. **The use of the *Specific Skill Series Placement Test* is recommended to determine the appropriate level.**

THE NEW EDITION:

The fifth edition of the *Specific Skill Series* maintains the quality and focus that has distinguished this program for more than 25 years. A key element central to the program's success has been the unique nature of the reading selections. Nonfiction pieces about current topics have been designed to stimulate the interest of students, motivating them to use the comprehension strategies they have learned to further their reading. To keep this important aspect of the program intact, a percentage of the reading selections have been replaced in order to ensure the continued relevance of the subject material.

In addition, a significant percentage of the artwork in the program has been replaced to give the books a contemporary look. The cover photographs are designed to appeal to readers of all ages.

SESSIONS:

Short practice sessions are the most effective. It is desirable to have a practice session every day or every other day, using a few units each session.

SCORING:

Pupils should record their answers on the reproducible worksheets. The worksheets make scoring easier and provide uniform records of the pupils' work. Using worksheets also avoids consuming the exercise books.

It is important for pupils to know how well they are doing. For this reason, units should be scored as soon as they have been completed. Then a discussion can be held in which pupils justify their choices. (The Integrated Language Activities, many of which are open-ended, do not lend themselves to an objective score; thus there are no answer keys for these pages.)

GENERAL INFORMATION ON *LOCATING THE ANSWER*:

At the earlier levels the answer to the question is worded much the same as the question itself. As the books increase in difficulty, there is less correspondence between the phrasing of the question and the phrasing of the answer.

SUGGESTED STEPS:

1. Pupils read the question *first* and then look for the answer.

2. Pupils use the range finder (sentence choices) in Books B–H. The letters or numbers in the range finder (below the question) indicate which sentences must be read to locate the answer to the question. In the Picture Level, the pupils decide which picture answers the question. For Preparatory and A levels, the number before the question tells the paragraph to read.

3. Pupils read the sentences with the question in mind. (On the Picture Level, pupils look at the pictures. On the Preparatory and A levels, pupils read the paragraph.)

4. When using Books B–H, pupils write (in the space on the worksheet) the letter or number of the sentence that answers the question. On the Picture Level, pupils write the letter of the correct picture choice. On the Preparatory and A levels, pupils write the letter of the correct word choice.

Additional information on using LOCATING THE ANSWER with pupils will be found in the **Specific Skill Series Teacher's Manual**.

RELATED MATERIALS:

Specific Skill Series Placement Tests, which enable the teacher to place pupils at their appropriate levels in each skill, are available for the Elementary (Pre-1–6) and Midway (4–8) grade levels.

About This Book

Reading to find out about something is different from other reading. First you look for a page that will give you the answer you want. Then you read carefully. You think about what you want to find out.

Knowing what to look for when you read is important. You need to read with your questions in mind. It is like looking for something you have lost. You don't know where the lost thing is. But you know what you are looking for.

For each unit in this book, you will see a story and eight questions. The answers to the questions are in the story. Your job is to find **where** the answers are. You do not answer the questions. Instead, you tell which sentence gives the answer.

Read the sentences below. Find the sentence that gives the answer to this question: "How many states are larger than Texas?"

(**A**) Texas is a very large state. (**B**) Only one state is larger. (**C**) Alaska is larger than Texas. (**D**) Texas has many more people than Alaska, though.

The answer is in sentence (**B**). Did you find it?

As you do each unit, read the questions first. Then look for the answers. Read the sentences with the question in mind. Then tell which sentence gives the answer.

UNIT 1
The Airline Workers

(A) Airlines have many different kinds of workers. (B) The airline workers have special suits. (C) Pilots, copilots, workers at the airport, and helpers on the airplane may also wear the same colors. (D) They wear "wings" on their suit jackets. (E) The "wings" show what their jobs are and what airline they work for.

(F) At the airport there are special workers. (G) Some sell tickets. (H) Others weigh and check the bags of passengers. (I) Ground workers are busy getting the planes ready. (J) They are putting gas and food into the airplanes.

(K) Workers on an airplane help people find their seats. (L) They help put coats up above and small bags under the seats. (M) They show passengers how to fasten their seat belts. (N) They serve food and drinks to people.

(O) The pilot flies the airplane. (P) The copilot helps the pilot. (Q) A flight engineer makes sure that the engines and all parts of the plane are working just right.

(R) Workers in the control tower tell the pilot about the weather. (S) They also tell the pilot which runway to use. (T) After takeoff the pilot talks to a radio operator in the tower. (U) The pilot lets the operator know where the plane is at all times. (V) When the pilot is ready to land, the tower workers help again. (W) They tell the pilot when all is clear for the landing.

UNIT 1
The Airline Workers

1. What do airline workers wear to look special?
   Sentence   (**A**)   (**B**)   (**C**)

2. What do airline workers wear on their jackets?
   Sentence   (**D**)   (**E**)   (**F**)

3. Who gets the planes ready on the ground?
   Sentence   (**G**)   (**H**)   (**I**)

4. Where do small bags go?
   Sentence   (**J**)   (**K**)   (**L**)

5. Who flies the airplane?
   Sentence   (**M**)   (**N**)   (**O**)

6. Who makes sure that the engines are running just right?
   Sentence   (**P**)   (**Q**)   (**R**)

7. What does the pilot do after takeoff?
   Sentence   (**S**)   (**T**)   (**U**)

8. Does the pilot get an "all-clear" signal to land?
   Sentence   (**U**)   (**V**)   (**W**)

UNIT 2
The House Painters

(**A**) People like the housepainters to come. (**B**) They make old houses look new again. (**C**) They make everything look clean and bright with their brushes and buckets of paint.

(**D**) Housepainters have a lot to do before they can even start to paint. (**E**) First they must make the sides of the house smooth so that the paint will go on easily. (**F**) They take off all old lumps of dry paint. (**G**) To do this they use scrapers and sandpaper. (**H**) They also fill in the cracks.

(**I**) The painters must get their brushes ready. (**J**) Brushes must be clean. (**K**) They must be soft. (**L**) The bushes and grass around the house must be covered so they won't get splashed with paint. (**M**) The painters use a canvas to do this. (**N**) The painters must also mix their paints. (**O**) They mix them until they are just the right color. (**P**) They mix them so that they will not be too thick or too thin. (**Q**) This takes lots of time.

(**R**) The painters are then ready to put on the first coat of paint. (**S**) They must climb up ladders. (**T**) On goes the first coat, covering the old paint. (**U**) Then comes the second coat of paint, making the house look even better.

(**V**) When the work is done, the painters clean up and put things away. (**W**) Everybody says, "How pretty you have made our house look! (**X**) Thank you, housepainters."

UNIT 2
The House Painters

1. How do the housepainters make old houses look?
    Sentence   (**A**)   (**B**)   (**C**)

2. What do the painters do first?
    Sentence   (**D**)   (**E**)   (**F**)

3. How do the painters get the dry paint off?
    Sentence   (**G**)   (**H**)   (**I**)

4. Should the paintbrushes be hard?
    Sentence   (**J**)   (**K**)   (**L**)

5. With what are the bushes and grass covered?
    Sentence   (**M**)   (**N**)   (**O**)

6. Does mixing paints take much time?
    Sentence   (**P**)   (**Q**)   (**R**)

7. What does the first coat cover?
    Sentence   (**S**)   (**T**)   (**U**)

8. When do the painters clean up?
    Sentence   (**V**)   (**W**)   (**X**)

(**A**) Some people who work in the library are called librarians. (**B**) The librarians help people find the books they want. (**C**) The librarians put books on the right shelves. (**D**) They are very busy people.

(**E**) The librarians keep books on the same subjects together. (**F**) Books about animals are kept in the same place. (**G**) Books about airplanes are kept together. (**H**) Books about boats are kept together. (**I**) This helps people find books much faster.

(**J**) The librarians know which books people like the best. (**K**) Librarians read many books themselves. (**L**) They read what people have to say about books. (**M**) This helps them find out which books to buy for the library.

(**N**) The librarians know which books have been taken out of the library. (**O**) They keep a computer file for every book. (**P**) Some people don't bring back the books on time. (**Q**) Librarians check the files and ask those people to pay a quarter for each day the books are overdue. (**R**) When the books are brought back, they are put on the shelves. (**S**) Special library assistants do this work. (**T**) They want each book to be in the right place.

(**U**) It makes librarians happy to see people take out books. (**V**) Be sure to ask them for help, if you need it. (**W**) Above all, take good care of the books. (**X**) As the librarians say, "Others will want to read them."

UNIT 3
The Librarians

1. Where do the librarians put books?
   Sentence   (A)   (B)   (C)

2. Are books on the same subject kept together?
   Sentence   (D)   (E)   (F)

3. Where are books about boats kept?
   Sentence   (G)   (H)   (I)

4. Do librarians read many books?
   Sentence   (J)   (K)   (L)

5. Do librarians know which books are out?
   Sentence   (M)   (N)   (O)

6. How much money do people pay on overdue books?
   Sentence   (P)   (Q)   (R)

7. Who puts the books on the shelves?
   Sentence   (S)   (T)   (U)

8. Should you ask the librarians for help?
   Sentence   (V)   (W)   (X)

UNIT 4
The Farmers

(A) Farmers work on a farm. (B) They may grow fruits and vegetables. (C) They may raise animals. (D) They work hard so that people get good food to eat.

(E) In the spring farmers turn over the soil with their tractors. (F) They feed the soil so that plants will grow better. (G) They plant the seeds. (H) All spring and summer they work to keep the weeds away. (I) They make sure that the crops get plenty of water. (J) Sometimes they have airplanes fly over their farms to spray the crops and kill the bugs. (K) Farmers must see that the fruits and vegetables are picked. (L) Then they send them to market.

(M) Farmers raise pigs so that people will have pork chops and bacon to eat. (N) Farmers raise sheep to give people food and clothing. (O) They raise chickens so people will have eggs for breakfast. (P) They raise cows to give milk, cream, butter, and cheese.

(Q) Farmers must give the animals much care. (R) Animals must be fed and kept clean. (S) They need a good place to stay at night.

(T) Farmers like their work. (U) They like to work with animals. (V) They like to see plants grow. (W) They want to work outdoors in the fresh air and sunshine. (X) At the end of their long day's work, farmers are tired but happy.

1. What do the farmers grow?
   Sentence   (A)   (B)   (C)

2. Why does the farmer work hard?
   Sentence   (D)   (E)   (F)

3. Do the crops get plenty of water?
   Sentence   (G)   (H)   (I)

4. Why do airplanes fly over the farms?
   Sentence   (J)   (K)   (L)

5. What comes from pigs?
   Sentence   (M)   (N)   (O)

6. Where does milk come from?
   Sentence   (P)   (Q)   (R)

7. Do farmers like their work?
   Sentence   (S)   (T)   (U)

8. Do farmers like the sunshine?
   Sentence   (V)   (W)   (X)

(A) The supermarket has many workers to help people buy the food they want. (B) Some of the supermarket helpers put the food on the shelves. (C) Some workers put the food into bags. (D) Other supermarket workers do other jobs.

(E) All day long people take food from the shelves. (F) The food must be replaced. (G) If it were not, there would be nothing left to buy. (H) First the food is brought up from the storeroom. (I) Then the cans and boxes are taken to the right places in the store. (J) They are placed on the right shelves. (K) This takes time. (L) It takes many workers to keep the shelves full.

(M) Meat and fish are often found at the back of the supermarket. (N) The meat is cut into pieces, wrapped, and put into the showcase. (O) The fish is kept on ice.

(P) It is easy for people to find the kinds of food they want. (Q) There is a place for fruits and vegetables. (R) There is a dairy department with milk, cream, butter, eggs, and cheese. (S) There is also a frozen food department.

(T) After the people take the food they need, they go to a checkout counter. (U) The cashier tells them how much to pay. (V) The food is put into a bag. (W) The shopping is done. (X) Supermarket workers have been a big help.

1. Who puts food on the shelves?
    Sentence   (A)   (B)   (C)

2. What do people take off the shelves?
    Sentence   (D)   (E)   (F)

3. In which room is the food stored?
    Sentence   (G)   (H)   (I)

4. Are the cans and boxes stacked quickly?
    Sentence   (J)   (K)   (L)

5. Where are meat and fish often found?
    Sentence   (M)   (N)   (O)

6. What is found in the dairy department?
    Sentence   (P)   (Q)   (R)

7. Who tells the people how much to pay?
    Sentence   (S)   (T)   (U)

8. Is the food put into a bag?
    Sentence   (V)   (W)   (X)

(A) What do workers at gas stations do? (B) Workers at self-service gas stations may just take people's money. (C) At full-service gas stations workers do other jobs. (D) Some gas stations have both types of services.

(E) Workers at self-service stations do the same job as people working in many stores. (F) They take people's money. (G) Some people pay with plastic credit cards. (H) Often these workers sit in a small booth. (I) They turn the gas pump on and off. (J) Sometimes they use a computer. (K) The driver pays and puts gas into the car.

(L) Workers at full-service stations do many different jobs. (M) They put the gas into the cars. (N) They also wash the car windows. (O) This helps the driver see better. (P) The workers will find out how much oil is in the car if someone asks them to check it.

(Q) Sometimes cars need work done on them. (R) People can bring their cars to full-service stations to be fixed. (S) If a car won't start, a tow truck might have to bring it to the station.

(T) "We could be called car doctors," say some gas station workers. (U) Sometimes people bring in their cars just for "checkups." (V) Other times the workers must find out what is wrong with the car. (W) Then they work on the car until it is "better." (X) They might need a few minutes or a few hours!

UNIT 6
The Gas Station Workers

1. Where do workers do more than one job?
   Sentence   (A)   (B)   (C)

2. What do workers at self-service stations take from people?
   Sentence   (D)   (E)   (F)

3. Who turns the pumps on and off at self-service stations?
   Sentence   (G)   (H)   (I)

4. Are all jobs at full-service stations the same?
   Sentence   (J)   (K)   (L)

5. Who puts gas into the cars?
   Sentence   (M)   (N)   (O)

6. What, besides gas, do cars need inside them?
   Sentence   (P)   (Q)   (R)

7. What else could gas station workers be called?
   Sentence   (S)   (T)   (U)

8. Do workers work on a car after it is all better?
   Sentence   (V)   (W)   (X)

```
                    Foods-to-Go
     cheese sandwich                    $1.25
     tuna sandwich                      $1.25
     peanut butter sandwich             $1.00
     chicken soup with rice             $1.30
                    * * * *
     fresh fruit                        $ .60
     carrot cake                        $1.25
     blackberry cupcake                 $ .50
                    * * * *
     glass of milk or cup of hot tea    $ .50
```

A. Exercising Your Skill

You are going to buy lunch at the Foods-to-Go store. Read the foods you can choose in the list above. Then answer these questions on your paper.

1. How much does chicken soup with rice cost?
2. How many different sandwiches can you buy? What are they?
3. How much does fresh fruit cost?
4. Can you buy apple pie?
5. Can you buy popcorn?
6. How many different drinks can you buy? What are they?

B. Expanding Your Skill

Look at the foods listed in the box. Can you buy any of these foods at the Foods-to-Go store? On your paper, list the foods in the box that you can get there. Add other foods you like to eat.

```
    fruit      blackberry cupcake      corn
```

C. Exploring Language

Read each story. Answer the questions. Find the answers in the list in Part A.

1.   "I'm ready for lunch," said Max. "I want to eat a fish sandwich."

   What kind of sandwich should Max eat?

2.   "It's cold this morning," said Max's mother. "I really need something hot to drink."

   What should Max's mother drink?

3.   "Since we're going on a hike this afternoon, I really want a large lunch!" Dad said. "I think I'll have a cup of chicken soup, two tuna sandwiches, three blackberry cupcakes, and a large mug of coffee."

   Can Dad get all these things at the Foods-to-Go store? What can he not get there?

D. Expressing Yourself

Do one of these things.

1. Make believe that you are going to open a food store. Draw a picture of foods you will sell in your store. Write the names of the foods in your picture.

2. Make up some funny foods that you really could not eat, but you can pretend to eat. Here are some funny foods: mud pie, blackberry dandelions, and toad toast.

UNIT 7
The Cleaners

(A) Some people press and clean our clothes. (B) They are called cleaners. (C) It is their job to help us look our best.

(D) A clerk at the counter takes the clothes. (E) The clerk lists our name, address, and the date. (F) The clerk puts down the colors and kinds of clothes we bring in. (G) On the same list the clerk writes down what is to be done. (H) We get a copy of this list to take with us.

(I) Sometimes we just want our clothes pressed. (J) Other times we want our clothes cleaned. (K) When clothes are to be cleaned, spots are taken out first. (L) The clothes are not washed in water. (M) They are run through a special cleaning machine. (N) Big presses are used to iron the clothes. (O) After they are pressed, the clothes are covered with see-through bags. (P) These bags keep the clothes from getting dusty. (Q) They also let us see if we are getting the right clothes back again!

(R) The clothes at the cleaners are hung in a certain order. (S) Clothes that are ready on the same day are kept together. (T) In this way the clerks can find the clothes quickly.

(U) When we go back to the cleaners, we hand in our copy of things to be done. (V) The clerk uses this to find our clothes. (W) The clerk brings us the clothes. (X) We pay for the job and take our clothes home.

1. How do cleaners make people look?
    Sentence   (A)   (B)   (C)

2. Who takes the clothes that are turned in?
    Sentence   (D)   (E)   (F)

3. Do we sometimes want our clothes just pressed?
    Sentence   (G)   (H)   (I)

4. What is done to the clothes first?
    Sentence   (J)   (K)   (L)

5. What is used to iron the clothes?
    Sentence   (M)   (N)   (O)

6. Can we see our clothes through the bags?
    Sentence   (P)   (Q)   (R)

7. Why are the clothes ready on the same day kept
    together?
    Sentence   (S)   (T)   (U)

8. Do we give the clerk money?
    Sentence   (V)   (W)   (X)

UNIT 8
The Photographers

(A) People who take pictures are called photographers. (B) The pictures they take are called photographs. (C) Some photographers are paid to take pictures. (D) Most of the pictures they take are of people. (E) Some pictures are in black and white, and others are in color. (F) People like color pictures best because they show everything as it really is.

(G) All of us like to have photographs in our houses. (H) They make us think of the people we like. (I) They may also help us think of the places we have seen. (J) In many homes there is a large family picture taken by the photographer. (K) Sometimes the photograph is just of the children.

(L) Mothers and fathers often want pictures taken of their baby. (M) The photographer knows how to get a baby to smile and laugh. (N) Sometimes the baby is given something to play with. (O) The photographer may make a funny sound. (P) The baby smiles and—"click"—the picture is taken.

(Q) Photographers don't like people to look right at the camera. (R) They ask them to turn a little. (S) They often talk to people who are having their pictures taken. (T) They don't want people to look afraid or stiff.

(U) Photographers know a lot about cameras. (V) They know just how much light to use. (W) They know how to get people to look their best. (X) As one photographer said, "Good pictures just don't happen by chance."

1. What are the pictures called?
   Sentence (**A**)   (**B**)   (**C**)

2. Why do people like color pictures best?
   Sentence (**D**)   (**E**)   (**F**)

3. Do pictures make us think of people?
   Sentence (**G**)   (**H**)   (**I**)

4. Do photographers ever take large family pictures?
   Sentence (**J**)   (**K**)   (**L**)

5. What may the photographer give the baby?
   Sentence (**M**)   (**N**)   (**O**)

6. What happens when the baby smiles?
   Sentence (**P**)   (**Q**)   (**R**)

7. Do photographers know much about cameras?
   Sentence (**S**)   (**T**)   (**U**)

8. What can photographers get people to do?
   Sentence (**V**)   (**W**)   (**X**)

(A) The police look after people and the things they own. (B) They help keep people safe. (C) They keep their things from being broken or taken. (D) Their jobs are not easy, but the police like helping people.

(E) The police get around town in many ways. (F) Some walk, some go by car, and others ride on motorcycles. (G) In the big cities some of the police ride on horses. (H) They must go around the town to see that everything is all right.

(I) As they go around the town, the police help people. (J) Sometimes they find lost children. (K) They find out where the children live. (L) They take the children home. (M) If the police see people fighting, they put a stop to it right away. (N) People often ask a police officer how to get to a certain place in the town. (O) Police can always tell the people which way to go. (P) Everyone on the police force knows all the streets and roads very well.

(Q) Some police guards stand at crossings. (R) They are called traffic police. (S) They tell the cars when to go and when to stop. (T) They make sure the cars do not go too fast. (U) They help old people and children cross the street.

(V) The police must be brave and strong to do their jobs. (W) They must work very hard. (X) The police like their work because they enjoy helping people.

1. Do police watch over people and their things?
   Sentence   **(A)**   **(B)**   **(C)**

2. Are the jobs of the police hard?
   Sentence   **(D)**   **(E)**   **(F)**

3. Why must the police go around a town?
   Sentence   **(G)**   **(H)**   **(I)**

4. Where do the police take lost children?
   Sentence   **(J)**   **(K)**   **(L)**

5. What do people often ask a police officer?
   Sentence   **(M)**   **(N)**   **(O)**

6. Where do some police officers stand?
   Sentence   **(P)**   **(Q)**   **(R)**

7. Do the police help children cross the street?
   Sentence   **(S)**   **(T)**   **(U)**

8. Why do the police like their work?
   Sentence   **(V)**   **(W)**   **(X)**

(A) People who fix hair are called hairdressers. (B) They work in shops with bright lights, sinks, mirrors, dryers, and other tools for fixing hair. (C) Hairdressers wash, dry, cut, color, straighten, wave, and comb hair.

(D) Special training is needed to become a hairdresser. (E) Hairdressing schools teach how to wash and cut hair. (F) Students learn to care for different kinds of hair. (G) They learn about hair colors, creams, and oils. (H) They learn to keep hair attractive and healthy.

(I) Washing the hair is the same as giving a shampoo. (J) The hair and head are rubbed with soapy suds. (K) Clear water is used to wash away the suds. (L) When the hair squeaks, a hairdresser knows it is clean.

(M) After getting a shampoo, some people want hairdressers to change the color of their hair. (N) Others want waves or curls that will last a long time. (O) Many people just have their hair washed, cut, and blown dry. (P) Others have their hair straightened or curled. (Q) Sometimes the hair is set with curlers. (R) Then the customer must sit under the dryer until the hair is dry.

(S) Hairdressers keep up with the latest hairstyles. (T) Styles worn by famous people may become popular. (U) A woman customer may want her hair styled like that of a rock star. (V) A male customer may want the hairstyle of a famous sports figure. (W) Both men and women want their hairdressers to give them a brand new look.

UNIT 10
The Hairdressers

1. Where do hairdressers work?
   Sentence   (A)   (B)   (C)

2. Do hairdressers need any training?
   Sentence   (D)   (E)   (F)

3. Do hairdressers learn how to keep hair healthy?
   Sentence   (G)   (H)   (I)

4. When is the hair clean?
   Sentence   (J)   (K)   (L)

5. Is hair ever blown dry?
   Sentence   (M)   (N)   (O)

6. What must the customer do when curlers are used?
   Sentence   (P)   (Q)   (R)

7. How might some women want their hair styled?
   Sentence   (S)   (T)   (U)

8. Do sports figures affect hairstyles?
   Sentence   (U)   (V)   (W)

UNIT 11
The Street Workers

(A) In towns and cities people pay money to have the streets taken care of. (B) Some street workers drive machines that clean the streets. (C) Other street workers fix bumpy or broken streets. (D) In the fall street workers take the leaves off the streets. (E) In the winter they plow snow off the streets.

(F) Street workers keep the streets clean. (G) Sometimes they wash the streets. (H) They use big water trucks. (I) The trucks splash water over the dusty streets. (J) The street cleaners also drive trucks with large brushes. (K) The brushes sweep the streets. (L) They sweep the dirt into the trucks.

(M) Other street workers fix holes in the streets. (N) They fill dump trucks with material for filling the holes. (O) After a hole is filled, they smooth out the top with tough material. (P) They make sure that the road will not be bumpy.

(Q) When fall comes, street workers take away piles of leaves. (R) People rake their leaves and put them in piles on the sides of the street. (S) The street cleaners put the leaves in large trucks and take them away.

(T) In the winter the street workers spread sand or salt on icy streets. (U) When there is snow, they get out the snow plows. (V) The plows push the snow to the sides of the streets. (W) The street workers keep the streets clear for cars, trucks, and buses. (X) Street workers are busy all year long.

UNIT 11
The Street Workers

1. For what do people in towns and cities pay money?
   Sentence   (A)   (B)   (C)

2. What do street workers take off streets in the fall?
   Sentence   (D)   (E)   (F)

3. What do they use to wash the streets?
   Sentence   (G)   (H)   (I)

4. What is used to sweep the streets?
   Sentence   (J)   (K)   (L)

5. Who fixes holes in the streets?
   Sentence   (M)   (N)   (O)

6. What do people in towns and cities do with their leaves?
   Sentence   (P)   (Q)   (R)

7. When are snow plows taken out?
   Sentence   (S)   (T)   (U)

8. What do the snow plows do?
   Sentence   (V)   (W)   (X)

UNIT 12
The Letter Carriers

(A) The letter carriers bring us mail. (B) We see them coming from far away. (C) Many wear blue uniforms. (D) We know them by their big, strong bags. (E) We all know the letter carriers, but do we know the story of how those letters got into their bags? (F) Do we know all about their job?

(G) People at the post office sort the mail at night. (H) Letters for the same parts of town are kept together. (I) In the morning the letter carriers pick up their letters. (J) They know which houses come first, next, and last. (K) They put the letters in order. (L) This takes the carriers about one hour.

(M) Then the letter carriers put the letters into their bags. (N) They cannot always get all of their mail into one bag. (O) A truck takes their other letters to big, blue boxes on streets where they work. (P) The letters stay there until the carriers pick them up.

(Q) Sometimes letter carriers walk to the parts of town where they give out mail. (R) Other carriers may have to go far from the post office. (S) They may ride in mail trucks. (T) Some carriers may ride in streetcars or buses.

(U) When they get to their parts of town, the letter carriers begin their trips from house to house. (V) They know everyone. (W) Everyone waits for their friendly smiles. (X) Everyone hopes for some letters.

1. What color are letter carriers' uniforms?
    Sentence   (A)   (B)   (C)

2. Do the letter carriers have large bags?
    Sentence   (D)   (E)   (F)

3. When is the mail sorted?
    Sentence   (G)   (H)   (I)

4. Do the letter carriers put their letters in order?
    Sentence   (J)   (K)   (L)

5. In what kinds of boxes are the letters kept?
    Sentence   (M)   (N)   (O)

6. Do letter carriers ever walk to their parts of town?
    Sentence   (P)   (Q)   (R)

7. Do letter carriers ever ride on buses?
    Sentence   (S)   (T)   (U)

8. What do people want letter carriers to bring?
    Sentence   (V)   (W)   (X)

The State Fair

<u>Animal Shows</u>	<u>Best Baked Foods</u>	<u>Places for Help</u>
Huge Cows	Apple Pies	First-Aid Stand
Baby Sheep	Corn Bread	Food Stand
Baby Pigs	Cheese Cakes	Ticket Stand

RIDES AND GAMES ARE BEHIND THE FOOD STAND

A. Exercising Your Skill

You have been waiting all year for this day. You are at the State Fair! The sign above is at the main gate. It lists what is at the fair. Read the sign. On your paper, write the answers to these questions.

1. What kinds of baby animals can you see?
2. Where can you find fast rides?
3. Where can you go to buy a ticket?
4. Where would you go if you felt sick?
5. Where can you buy lunch?
6. How many animal shows can you see?

B. Expanding Your Skill

Which of the foods in the box will be part of the contest that picks the best food at the State Fair? On your paper, write the answers. On your list, add one more food that is part of the best food contest.

apple pie	corn bread	blackberry cupcakes

C. Exploring Language

Copy this story on your paper. Fill in the answers. Find the answers in the sign in Part A.

> Going to the State Fair is a great thing to do! First we buy our tickets at the _____ . I can't wait to see the baby _____ and _____ . Sometimes I bake an _____ pie to try to win the Best Baked Foods. At lunch we buy sandwiches at the _____ . Then we walk behind the Food Stand to go on all the _____ . I love the State Fair!

Now draw a picture to go with the story. Give your picture and story a name.

D. Expressing Yourself

Do one of these things.

1. Pretend you are going to the State Fair. Make a list of what you will do for the day. Use the sign to help you plan your day.

2. Draw a map of the fairgrounds. Put on it all the places listed on the sign. Use large paper and crayons if you can.

3. Write a story about a day at the fair. Tell what you did and one funny thing that happened.

4. Pretend that you are one of the animals at the fair or any other animal. Move around and make sounds like that animal. Let your classmates guess what animal you are pretending to be.

(A) Many people keep their money in banks. (B) Bankers are the men and women who run the banks. (C) Other workers help the bankers. (D) Some of these workers work at the bank windows. (E) Others write letters and answer the telephones. (F) Others make sure the bank's machines run well.

(G) Bank workers must be very careful workers. (H) They must be able to work well with numbers. (I) They use computers to help them keep track of money.

(J) The workers at bank windows are called tellers. (K) When people want to put in or take out money, they can go to a teller. (L) The teller can let people know how much money they have saved. (M) Banks also have machines where people can take money out of their accounts.

(N) Most people use bank checks instead of money. (O) They put their money in the bank. (P) Then the bank gives them a book of checks. (Q) When they go to stores or pay bills, people write checks to pay for things. (R) The bank pays the stores. (S) Then the bank subtracts that amount from the money the person has put in the bank.

(T) Sometimes the banker will give people money to buy something. (U) This is called a loan. (V) The people must sign a paper saying they will pay the money back to the bank. (W) After the people pay everything they owe, the loan is cancelled. (X) This is just another way bank workers help people.

UNIT 13
The Bank Workers

1. Who helps the bankers run the banks?
   Sentence   (**A**)   (**B**)   (**C**)

2. Are there workers at the bank windows?
   Sentence   (**D**)   (**E**)   (**F**)

3. Do bank workers have to work well with numbers?
   Sentence   (**G**)   (**H**)   (**I**)

4. Who can tell people how much they have saved?
   Sentence   (**J**)   (**K**)   (**L**)

5. What do some people use instead of money?
   Sentence   (**M**)   (**N**)   (**O**)

6. Where can people write checks to pay for things?
   Sentence   (**P**)   (**Q**)   (**R**)

7. What is a loan?
   Sentence   (**S**)   (**T**)   (**U**)

8. When do people no longer owe money to the bank?
   Sentence   (**V**)   (**W**)   (**X**)

UNIT 14
The Pet Shop Owners

(A) The pet shop owners have jobs that many children would like to have. (B) Their work sometimes seems like play. (C) Most children like animals. (D) The pet shop owners like animals too, but they really have to work hard to take care of them.

(E) Every day the owners of pet shops must feed all the animals in their shops. (F) This is more work than getting dinner ready for a big family. (G) At home everyone eats the same kind of food. (H) In pet shops all the animals do not get the same things to eat.

(I) Pet shop owners work hard to keep the shop clean. (J) The pets must be washed. (K) Some animals need haircuts. (L) The cages must be cleaned. (M) The floor must be swept.

(N) Pet shop owners need to know a lot about animals. (O) Children often need help in choosing the right pets. (P) They ask pet shop owners many questions. (Q) Some want to know all about dogs. (R) Some want to know what to feed the cat. (S) Others want to know how to make a parrot talk.

(T) The owners like children to come to their shops. (U) They have fun watching them with the animals. (V) "You always know when they have found the right pet," says one pet shop owner. (W) "Smiles come to their faces, and their eyes light up. (X) Even the animal seems to know that it is about to have a new home."

1. Would some children like to own pet shops?
    Sentence   (A)   (B)   (C)

2. How often must the pets be fed?
    Sentence   (D)   (E)   (F)

3. Do all pets eat the same kind of food?
    Sentence   (G)   (H)   (I)

4. What must be done to the cages?
    Sentence   (J)   (K)   (L)

5. What kind of help do children often need in pet shops?
    Sentence   (M)   (N)   (O)

6. Do the children ask many questions?
    Sentence   (P)   (Q)   (R)

7. Do the owners like to watch the children?
    Sentence   (S)   (T)   (U)

8. What happens to the faces of the children?
    Sentence   (V)   (W)   (X)

(A) Plumbers often work in the kitchens, bathrooms, and cellars of homes. (B) They stop water from running when it is supposed to be turned off. (C) They fix sinks and toilets that are stopped up. (D) They patch cracks in pipes. (E) Sometimes they put in new pipes.

(F) Special tools are used by the plumbers. (G) Some tools have to fit around very large pipes. (H) Other tools are used to work on smaller pipes. (I) Certain tools are used to clean out curved pipes. (J) There are also tools that force water or dirt out of pipes.

(K) When people find water in the cellar, they call a plumber. (L) The plumber finds out where the water is coming from. (M) Maybe a pipe has a small hole that needs patching. (N) If the pipe is badly cracked or broken, the plumber must put a new pipe in its place.

(O) People may also call plumbers if the heat in the house goes off. (P) Plumbers understand how the house is heated. (Q) They know which pipes carry heat through the house. (R) They know which pipes carry hot water or steam. (S) They know which pipes carry gas or oil.

(T) Plumbers help keep people's houses safe. (U) They help get rid of harmful germs. (V) They make sure that fresh water flows into the house. (W) They also make sure that waste water flows out of the house. (X) Plumbers make homes easy to live in.

1. Where do plumbers work?
    Sentence   (A)   (B)   (C)

2. Are special tools used by plumbers?
    Sentence   (D)   (E)   (F)

3. With what are the curved pipes cleaned?
    Sentence   (G)   (H)   (I)

4. Are special tools used to force out dirt?
    Sentence   (J)   (K)   (L)

5. Do people call plumbers to get heat in a house?
    Sentence   (M)   (N)   (O)

6. Do plumbers know if pipes carry steam?
    Sentence   (P)   (Q)   (R)

7. Who helps keep houses safe?
    Sentence   (S)   (T)   (U)

8. What do plumbers make sure flows out of the house?
    Sentence   (V)   (W)   (X)

(A) Doctors take care of people who are sick. (B) They try to find out what is wrong. (C) Sometimes they can tell what is wrong after a quick look. (D) Often they must spend more time checking. (E) They may even have to give tests to find out what is the matter.

(F) Doctors find out what is making people sick. (G) They tell people what to do to get well. (H) They may give medicine. (I) They may tell a person to rest. (J) They often tell a person which foods to eat. (K) People should do what doctors tell them to do. (L) They will get well sooner.

(M) People who are very sick or badly hurt may be sent to the hospital. (N) Many of the doctors at the hospital are specialists. (O) A specialist is a doctor who knows a lot about any one part of the body.

(P) There is a heart specialist for the person with a weak heart. (Q) There is a bone specialist for a person with a broken leg. (R) The specialists can give the best care at a hospital. (S) There they have everything they need to help.

(T) Sick people learn to trust their doctors. (U) Their doctors are their friends. (V) Their doctors are their helpers. (W) Their doctors give them the care they need. (X) Their doctors help them get well and strong again.

1. Who takes care of sick people?
    Sentence   (**A**)   (**B**)   (**C**)

2. Do doctors give tests?
    Sentence   (**D**)   (**E**)   (**F**)

3. What do doctors give sick people?
    Sentence   (**G**)   (**H**)   (**I**)

4. Why should people do what the doctors say?
    Sentence   (**J**)   (**K**)   (**L**)

5. What is a specialist?
    Sentence   (**M**)   (**N**)   (**O**)

6. Who would help fix a broken leg?
    Sentence   (**P**)   (**Q**)   (**R**)

7. What do specialists have at the hospital?
    Sentence   (**S**)   (**T**)   (**U**)

8. Who gives people the care they need?
    Sentence   (**V**)   (**W**)   (**X**)

(**A**) Do you know what is one of the biggest problems in many towns and cities? (**B**) It is trash! (**C**) Keeping towns and cities clean is a big job, and trash collectors are very important workers.

(**D**) Most people put trash into cans or bags. (**E**) They leave the cans or bags outside on certain days. (**F**) Trash collectors come along in big trucks. (**G**) They throw the trash into the trucks. (**H**) A machine inside the truck presses the trash together.

(**I**) Sometimes people throw away very large things, like washing machines or beds. (**J**) The people cannot fit these large things into bags or cans. (**K**) Trash collectors come around on certain days to take away these things. (**L**) In some places people must pay extra money for this.

(**M**) Trash collectors also take trash from public places. (**N**) There are trash cans and baskets at parks, playgrounds, beaches, and street corners. (**O**) These are for people who don't want to be "litter bugs." (**P**) Trash collectors come along and empty these cans and baskets.

(**Q**) Where to put all the trash is a problem. (**R**) Trash is taken to dumps or special buildings. (**S**) But these places are becoming too full. (**T**) People are trying to figure out new ways to get rid of trash. (**U**) One important way is to recycle it. (**V**) This means using trash again in another way. (**W**) Even if our trash is recycled, trash collectors still have a big job to do. (**X**) People throw things away every day!

UNIT 17
The Trash Collectors

1. Do many towns and cities have big problems?
   Sentence   **(A)**   **(B)**   **(C)**

2. Where do people put trash on certain days?
   Sentence   **(D)**   **(E)**   **(F)**

3. Where do the trash collectors throw the trash?
   Sentence   **(G)**   **(H)**   **(I)**

4. When do trash collectors take away very large things?
   Sentence   **(J)**   **(K)**   **(L)**

5. What do trash collectors take away from public places?
   Sentence   **(M)**   **(N)**   **(O)**

6. Who empties these cans and baskets?
   Sentence   **(P)**   **(Q)**   **(R)**

7. What are people trying to figure out about trash?
   Sentence   **(S)**   **(T)**   **(U)**

8. What does *recycle* mean?
   Sentence   **(V)**   **(W)**   **(X)**

UNIT 18
The Bus Drivers

(A) Bus drivers take people on trips. (B) They may take them on short trips around town. (C) They may take children to school. (D) They may take people on long trips to faraway places.

(E) In a town bus drivers must be on the lookout at all times. (F) They must keep their eyes on the traffic lights. (G) They must know the names of the streets. (H) The drivers must also know the bus stops.

(I) When people get on a town bus, they put their money into a box. (J) Sometimes the driver has to give them change. (K) The driver tells the people to move to the back of the bus. (L) As the bus makes stops, more people get on. (M) People can make more room by moving to the back of the bus.

(N) Drivers of school buses take children to school and home again. (O) They must be very good drivers. (P) They make sure that the children stay seated. (Q) The children must do this to keep safe.

(R) People going on long bus trips must have tickets. (S) The bus drivers take their tickets. (T) The drivers make sure everyone has a seat. (U) They know that the big bus will travel a long time. (V) They know they have a big job to do. (W) Bus drivers must keep everyone on the bus safe and happy. (X) They must take the people where they want to go.

1. Are all trips around town very long?
   Sentence   (**A**)   (**B**)   (**C**)

2. What must the drivers keep their eyes on?
   Sentence   (**D**)   (**E**)   (**F**)

3. Must the drivers know the bus stops?
   Sentence   (**G**)   (**H**)   (**I**)

4. What do the drivers tell the people?
   Sentence   (**J**)   (**K**)   (**L**)

5. Where does the school bus take children?
   Sentence   (**M**)   (**N**)   (**O**)

6. Why must children stay seated?
   Sentence   (**P**)   (**Q**)   (**R**)

7. Will the big bus travel a long time?
   Sentence   (**S**)   (**T**)   (**U**)

8. Must drivers keep the people on the bus safe and happy?
   Sentence   (**V**)   (**W**)   (**X**)

UNIT 19
The Rescue Workers

(A) Many people are injured in traffic accidents. (B) Others hurt themselves in falls. (C) Some people get burns in fires. (D) When accidents happen, rescue workers are called. (E) They travel in an ambulance. (F) The ambulance rings a siren to warn other drivers to pull over. (G) This helps the rescue workers get to injured people fast.

(H) Rescue workers are trained to do many things. (I) They can stop bleeding. (J) They can set broken bones with a splint. (K) They can help people who have stopped breathing. (L) It is important to do all these things fast.

(M) Sometimes rescue workers lift people carefully into the ambulance. (N) They use a stretcher to do this. (O) They may also put a brace around a person's neck or head. (P) This helps prevent more injury. (Q) Then the rescue workers drive the person to the hospital. (R) As they drive, they talk to hospital doctors by radio. (S) The doctors tell the workers what needs to be done. (T) The hospital workers get ready to receive the injured people. (U) The rescue workers tell the hospital when they will arrive.

(V) Does it surprise you to know that rescue workers also rescue animals? (W) An injured animal may be treated at home. (X) But it may have to go to an animal hospital. (Y) Some hospitals have ambulances to bring injured animals to them. (Z) Animals' doctors have much of the same equipment that humans' doctors do!

UNIT 19
The Rescue Workers

1. Do rescue workers help people who have fallen?
   Sentence   (A)   (B)   (C)

2. What do rescue workers travel in?
   Sentence   (D)   (E)   (F)

3. Can rescue workers help someone who is bleeding?
   Sentence   (G)   (H)   (I)

4. How do they set broken bones?
   Sentence   (J)   (K)   (L)

5. How do rescue workers lift a person into an ambulance?
   Sentence   (M)   (N)   (O)

6. Who do the rescue workers talk to from the ambulance?
   Sentence   (P)   (Q)   (R)

7. What do the hospital workers do?
   Sentence   (S)   (T)   (U)

8. Can an injured animal ever be treated at home?
   Sentence   (V)   (W)   (X)

Owl Lake Day Camp

Outside Fun	Inside Fun	Team Sports
hiking	drawing	basketball
swimming	singing	baseball
boating	dancing	kickball

ALL TENTS FOR RESTING ARE NEXT TO OWL LAKE.
ALL LUNCHES ARE EATEN IN THE BLUE ROOM IN
THE MAIN HOUSE!

A. Exercising Your Skill

It is your first day at camp. The sign above is at the main gate of Owl Lake Day Camp. It tells what you can do at the camp. Read the sign carefully. On your paper, write the answers to these questions.

1. How many team sports can you play at the camp?
2. What can you do outside?
3. What can you do inside?
4. Where can you go to eat lunch?
5. Where do you rest or take a nap?
6. Can you fly a kite at the camp?
7. How many outside sports take place in the water?

B. Expanding Your Skill

Add two more things to each list in Part A. Pick them from the words in the box below.

acting	climbing trees	football
fishing	running races	reading

C. Exploring Language

Read each story. On your paper, answer the questions. Find the answers in the sign in Part A. Answer in sentences, like this: *Young people will learn baseball at camp.*

1. "I'm worried about camp," May said to Jim. "The water scares me. I'd really feel proud if I could learn how to swim. Do you think I could?"

    How can May learn to like the water?

2. "Look at the list of things to do!" Sally said as she read the sign. "I love to play baseball. I wonder what other sports we'll learn at camp."

    What other sports will the young people learn at camp?

3. "I'm always hungry when I'm working hard at camp," Peter said to Hank. "Where do we go for meals?"

    Where should Peter go to eat?

D. Expressing Yourself

Do one of these things.

1. Write a letter. It can be to someone in your family or a friend. Tell about camp. Tell about your day. Tell what you like and do not like about camp. Use the sign in Part A to help you.

2. Draw a map of Owl Lake Day Camp. Be sure to include all the places listed on the sign at the main gate. Use large paper if you can.

3. Write a story about Owl Lake Day Camp. The story can be funny or scary. If you like, draw a picture to go with the story.

UNIT 20
The Carpenters

(A) People who work with wood are called carpenters. (B) Sometimes carpenters help build houses. (C) Sometimes they fix things that are broken. (D) Sometimes they make new things out of wood.

(E) Carpenters can make tables, chairs, desks, and bookcases. (F) They know how to do many things with wood. (G) They know how to cut the wood into small boards. (H) They do this with a saw. (I) Carpenters know how to put boards together. (J) They use a hammer and nails to do this. (K) They can make wood very smooth by rubbing it with sandpaper.

(L) Carpenters help build houses. (M) Some carpenters work at the big jobs on a house. (N) They put up the strong boards that help to hold up the house. (O) They hammer down the long boards to make the floors. (P) Other carpenters do some of the smaller jobs. (Q) They work on the doors, windows, and parts where smaller boards are needed.

(R) Carpenters fix things that are broken. (S) Sometimes a porch has loose boards. (T) The carpenter must hammer nails into the boards to keep them in place. (U) If a fence is falling down, the carpenter will put up new posts to make the fence strong again.

(V) Carpenters like to work with their hammers, nails, and saws. (W) They can make wood into any size and shape they want. (X) They say, "We can use our tools to make almost anything people need."

1. Do carpenters help build houses?
   Sentence   (A)   (B)   (C)

2. Who can make chairs and tables?
   Sentence   (D)   (E)   (F)

3. With what do carpenters cut wood?
   Sentence   (G)   (H)   (I)

4. How do they get the wood smooth?
   Sentence   (J)   (K)   (L)

5. What holds up the house?
   Sentence   (M)   (N)   (O)

6. Where are smaller boards needed?
   Sentence   (P)   (Q)   (R)

7. Why does the carpenter put in new posts?
   Sentence   (S)   (T)   (U)

8. What tools do carpenters use?
   Sentence   (V)   (W)   (X)

(A) Everyone knows when the firefighters are coming. (B) Big fire trucks speed down the street. (C) They are usually bright red. (D) Clanging bells let everyone know that the firefighters are on their way to a fire.

(E) How do firefighters get to a fire so fast? (F) The alarm rings at the fire station. (G) The firefighters hurry to their trucks. (H) Off they go to the fire. (I) As the fire trucks speed along, the firefighters put on their boots and rubber coats. (J) They put on large hats, called helmets. (K) When they get to the fire, they are ready to work.

(L) Many tools are kept on the fire truck. (M) There are hoses to shoot water into the fire. (N) There are axes to open doors and windows. (O) There are ladders to help the firefighters get up and down. (P) There are even nets for people to jump into.

(Q) When the truck gets to the fire, the firefighters drag off the hose. (R) They put it onto the fire hydrant. (S) Firefighters work fast to put out the fire. (T) They help people who are hurt or burned. (U) They make very sure the fire is out before they leave.

(V) When the firefighters get back to the fire station, they wash their trucks. (W) They get everything in order for the next call. (X) When the alarm sounds, they know it means, "Hurry, hurry. We need you!"

1. Do fire trucks go slowly down the street?
   Sentence   (**A**)   (**B**)   (**C**)

2. Where does the alarm ring?
   Sentence   (**D**)   (**E**)   (**F**)

3. When do the firefighters put on their coats?
   Sentence   (**G**)   (**H**)   (**I**)

4. What are helmets?
   Sentence   (**J**)   (**K**)   (**L**)

5. Why do fire trucks have axes?
   Sentence   (**M**)   (**N**)   (**O**)

6. What are the nets for?
   Sentence   (**P**)   (**Q**)   (**R**)

7. Which people do the firefighters help?
   Sentence   (**S**)   (**T**)   (**U**)

8. What does the alarm mean?
   Sentence   (**V**)   (**W**)   (**X**)

(A) Dentists make sure that teeth are healthy. (B) They look for holes in the teeth. (C) They check to see if teeth are straight. (D) Dentists also look at the gums to see if they are healthy.

(E) Dentists may take pictures of a person's teeth. (F) To do this, they use X-ray machines. (G) The pictures show how the teeth look on the inside. (H) The dentists look at these pictures. (I) The pictures help the dentists see if there is anything they must do.

(J) Most of the time, teeth just need to be cleaned. (K) Dentists have brushes and tools for doing this. (L) Some teeth have holes, called cavities. (M) Dentists use drills to clean out these holes. (N) When they have cleaned out the cavities, the dentists put in fillings.

(O) Sometimes dentists must pull a tooth. (P) They have the tools to do this. (Q) They can pull a tooth without the person feeling it.

(R) Dentists can tell if a person's teeth are well taken care of. (S) They can tell if the person eats the right foods. (T) They can tell if a person's teeth are brushed often. (U) Dentists say, "Brush your teeth three times a day. (V) Come to see us twice a year. (W) Your teeth will stay healthy. (X) You just need to take care of them."

1. What do dentists make sure of?
    Sentence   (**A**)   (**B**)   (**C**)

2. With what do they take pictures?
    Sentence   (**D**)   (**E**)   (**F**)

3. Do the pictures show the inside of teeth?
    Sentence   (**G**)   (**H**)   (**I**)

4. What are the holes in the teeth called?
    Sentence   (**J**)   (**K**)   (**L**)

5. Why does the dentist use a drill?
    Sentence   (**M**)   (**N**)   (**O**)

6. Does it hurt to have a tooth pulled?
    Sentence   (**P**)   (**Q**)   (**R**)

7. How often should people brush their teeth?
    Sentence   (**S**)   (**T**)   (**U**)

8. How often should people go to the dentist?
    Sentence   (**V**)   (**W**)   (**X**)

UNIT 23
The Movers

(A) People who help move the things we own are called movers. (B) Movers take furniture from one house to another. (C) Everybody knows that the movers are about to begin their work when they see the moving van coming down the street.

(D) Many things are in boxes for the movers. (E) Everything is ready to be taken out of the house. (F) In and out the movers go, taking the heavy furniture first. (G) Legs are taken off the beds and tables to make them easier to carry. (H) This also makes more room in the van.

(I) It is a big job to move a piano. (J) Two or three movers raise it. (K) They slide a dolly under it. (L) A dolly is a flat little wagon with small wheels. (M) Once the piano is on the dolly, the movers can roll it out of the house. (N) Up into the big van it goes.

(O) The movers are careful with furniture. (P) They cover it with thick pads. (Q) They don't want anything to happen to it. (R) Ropes help hold everything in place. (S) When the van is on the road, the movers don't want the furniture to slide around.

(T) Movers are strong. (U) They are also careful. (V) They know the best way to carry furniture. (W) "We take good care of furniture," say the movers. (X) "That's our job."

1. How do people know that the movers are coming?
   Sentence   (A)   (B)   (C)

2. Which furniture do the movers take first?
   Sentence   (D)   (E)   (F)

3. Is moving a piano easy?
   Sentence   (G)   (H)   (I)

4. What is a dolly?
   Sentence   (J)   (K)   (L)

5. How is the piano taken out of the house?
   Sentence   (M)   (N)   (O)

6. What helps hold everything in place?
   Sentence   (P)   (Q)   (R)

7. Are movers strong?
   Sentence   (S)   (T)   (U)

8. What do the movers know about carrying furniture?
   Sentence   (V)   (W)   (X)

(A) The telephone operators help us talk with other people on the telephone. (B) We get to know how they sound. (C) They are helpers we don't see very often.

(D) Telephone operators must talk well. (E) They say every word very slowly. (F) They say every word very clearly. (G) People like to hear them speak. (H) Their voices are friendly and pleasant.

(I) Sometimes we can't reach the person with whom we want to talk. (J) Then we get the operator. (K) The operator's number is "0." (L) Sometimes the operator is very busy and cannot talk with us right away. (M) Operators usually ask, "May I help you?"

(N) Telephone operators help find out why we can't reach people. (O) Sometimes we can't find a number in the phone book. (P) The operator can tell us what the number is. (Q) Sometimes when we can't reach someone, we think that person's phone isn't working. (R) The operator can check to see if the phone is out of order. (S) These are ways that telephone operators help us.

(T) How can we help the operators? (U) "There is one good way," they say. (V) "Talk slowly and clearly. (W) The telephone operators must first know what you are saying. (X) Then we can help you reach the person with whom you want to speak."

1. Do we see telephone operators often?
   Sentence   (**A**)   (**B**)   (**C**)

2. Do telephone operators talk slowly?
   Sentence   (**D**)   (**E**)   (**F**)

3. What do we like about the operators' voices?
   Sentence   (**G**)   (**H**)   (**I**)

4. What is the operator's number?
   Sentence   (**J**)   (**K**)   (**L**)

5. Do people always find a number in the phone book?
   Sentence   (**M**)   (**N**)   (**O**)

6. Who can check if a phone is out of order?
   Sentence   (**P**)   (**Q**)   (**R**)

7. Is there only one way that operators help us?
   Sentence   (**S**)   (**T**)   (**U**)

8. What must operators know first in order to help you?
   Sentence   (**V**)   (**W**)   (**X**)

(A) Teachers help children learn. (B) They know much that children do not know. (C) Teachers show the children how to read and write. (D) They teach children how to work with numbers. (E) They help them sing and draw.

(F) Children like to work in a nice room. (G) The teacher and children put up pictures to make the room look pretty. (H) The children may draw the pictures. (I) They like to see their own pictures on the wall.

(J) Teachers write many things on the chalkboard. (K) They show the children how to make letters and numbers. (L) At the start of the week, they may give children jobs. (M) Some children may be asked to water the plants, or empty the wastebasket, or pass out the books. (N) Teachers often write these jobs for the week on the chalkboard.

(O) Teachers tell children if they are doing good work. (P) They also tell them what they are doing wrong. (Q) Teachers mark papers. (R) They put marks on report cards. (S) Children take the report cards home. (T) Their parents read the report cards to see how the children are doing in school.

(U) Teachers want children to like school. (V) They know children will learn well if they like their school. (W) They know children will learn well if they listen and follow directions. (X) Teachers like to help children learn.

UNIT 25
The Teachers

1. Who teaches children to read?
   Sentence   (**A**)   (**B**)   (C)

2. Where do children like to work?
   Sentence   (**D**)   (**E**)   (F)

3. Who puts up the pictures?
   Sentence   (**G**)   (**H**)   (**I**)

4. When do teachers give children jobs?
   Sentence   (**J**)   (**K**)   (**L**)

5. Where do teachers write the jobs?
   Sentence   (**M**)   (**N**)   (**O**)

6. Who marks the papers?
   Sentence   (**P**)   (**Q**)   (**R**)

7. Why do parents read the report cards?
   Sentence   (**S**)   (**T**)   (**U**)

8. Why must children follow directions?
   Sentence   (**V**)   (**W**)   (**X**)

MAKE A PICTURE!   WIN A PRIZE!

Rules:

1. Draw a big picture.
2. Show one way to make your home a safe place.
3. Use lots of colors.

Give your picture to your teacher by March 1. The three winning pictures will be put up on the hall bulletin board on March 15.

- First Prize—a bat and ball
- Second Prize—a book
- Third Prize—a big box of crayons

A. Exercising Your Skill

Your school is having a picture contest. The sign above tells about it. Read the sign carefully. On your paper, write the answers to these questions.

1. What size picture should you make?
2. What should the picture show?
3. How many prizes are there?
4. What will you get if you win first prize?
5. When will the winning pictures be put up?
6. What is the second prize?

B. Expanding Your Skill

Read the words in the box. Which of these things could your picture show? Choose two things.

keeping things off stairs	feeding your cat
getting rid of newspapers	reading a book

C. Exploring Language

Read this list. It tells how to make your home a safe place.

- Pick up toys from the floor.
- Don't leave things on the stairs.
- Don't leave the stove turned on.
- Turn off the TV when nobody is watching it.
- Make sure cords are plugged in the right way.
- Keep on a high shelf things that are used to clean the floor or walls.
- Keep rags clean and throw out old, dirty rags.
- Keep important phone numbers close to the telephone.

Now talk about the list with a classmate. Why does each thing help make a home safe? Which have you done? Which things do you still need to do? Make a list of things you need to do when you go home. Add other safety ideas you can think of. Share your list with your classmates. See if your list and their lists are the same or different.

D. Expressing Yourself

Do one of these things.

1. You are the winner! Your picture won first prize in the contest. Draw the winning picture. Show one way to make your home a safe place. Remember to make your picture big and to use lots of colors!

2. Write your own set of home safety rules. Use your own words. Take your list home. Put it up where everyone in your family will see it.